TURN OVER ANY STONE

TURN OVER ANY STONE

BY EDNA HONG

Designed and illustrated
by Don Wallerstedt

AUGSBURG PUBLISHING HOUSE

Minneapolis, Minnesota

DEDICATION

To Judy, Pat, and Bob

and

all who are native citizens

of

Paindom

where I am but a tourist

CONTENTS

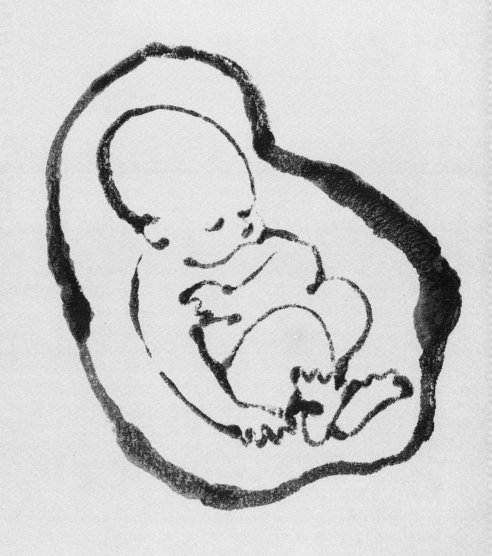

"Oh," she said, coming into the kitchen
where I had gone to punch down the bread dough.
"I almost don't like to see
my baby beside any other baby."

In the swift glint of tears I read
Naomi's sudden fear that time was carrying her
toward something she was unprepared to bear
but which would come all the same.
Her mind swooped and clutched the bat of fear
that had darted and dipped into its house
for the first time and hid it
in a secret solitary cell.

11

"Your bread is going over!" she laughed.
"I remember how you always forgot the bread rising
and how it grew over the edge of the big yellow bowl
and stretched and broke off in hunks,
and if a hunk of dough fell on the floor
you made a loaf of it and baked it
for whatever dog we happened to have at the time.
And when the bread was baked, we kids
smelled it and came tearing in and sometimes ate
the dog's loaf before anyone could warn us."

"It doesn't seem to have harmed you," I said.

"It was, is, and ever shall be
the best bread in the world," she said,
and went back to the living room,
where the two newest granddaughters,
born three months ago and thousands of miles apart,
lay side by side on the same blanket
for the first time. And the difference
between them was not simply and solely
that one was fair of skin and blonde of hair
and the other had thrush-brown skin and hair
and lashes of soft, lustrous black.
Plucking at the straying tatters of dough
and folding them back into the bowl,
I somehow knew that Nani, my beautiful
Hawaiian grandchild with the dark, inscrutable,
unlaughing eyes, concealed a mystery.
I knew that Naomi, my youngest daughter,
a stranger to the taste of grief,

was soon to give birth all over again—
this time to pain—
and her pain was already gathering
within my breast.
Nani, Nani, my pretty one,
are you bitter fruit?
A garbled and diminished self?
Did nature rudely abandon you
before you were finished and go on to something else?
Are you bewitched from your mother's womb?
Was there a sullen thirteenth fairy who, even before
your mother bore you for a long and happy life,
came with a cackling, crackling laugh
and wished you ill—
a future full of ill?
Did her evil wand touch the classical geometry
of genes that is an infant's body-birthright
and disorder it?

That tiny thumb set askew,
as if a worker at the assembly belt
in the womb factory fell asleep
momentarily
and blundered.
Does it mean other and hidden flaws?

You *do* see, we know, for your ebony eyes
follow the movements of life
but make no comment—
no comment whatsoever on life.

13

Your little cousin is already decoding
her environment, translating it into meaning.
Her merry blue eyes expound her critique.
Deep in her throat she advances her thesis
and propounds that life is good
and life is love.
But you, Nani,
I search your eyes in vain
for your deductions and inferences
and find enigma.
It seems to make no difference if we stay,
or go, or come back. Life seems to be
neither wondrous nor dull to you.
Does nothing mean anything?
Does everything mean nothing?

Do you hear?
Do your father's deep-toned, full-voweled
Hawaiian lullabies, his softly strumming
ukulele, find a clear but winding
path to your brain?

You cry—far too much,
your body tense and rigid,
and cannot be comforted.
Is this your commentary on life?

Nani, Nani,
born of love
born to love

14

laved in love
will the dim land of your consciousness
ever brighten to the waves of love
that caress its shores?

When I went to bed that night,
my pillowcase was rude, the sheets were harsh,
and there was no graciousness in the April moon.
Bats fly at night, and the bats of fear likewise.
Mine swooped in and out, dipped up and down,
kept sleep a far sigh away.

If my worst fears were true,
then why did this have to happen to Naomi,
our most vulnerable one—
this tender girl who had played with dolls
longer than the other ones, who had cut up all our Sears
and Montgomery Ward catalogues and created

for herself teeming families of unblemished infants
and flawless tots—an impeccable progeny,
American-dream families, complete
with handsome, virile, crewcut fathers
and Ford station wagons.
Why could Fate not leave this one's
little joys alone?

"I want to bring my baby home for the first time
in April," she had written.
"I want to be in Minnesota in April."

April—
but spring is ailing and Eden is burning.
The newborn leaf is seared and crimped,
forever dead to green
forever dead to life.

About midnight Naomi came into the bedroom
quietly and lay in her absent father's place;
how I wished that he were not away at this time!

"Mom, do you think that my baby is all right?"

"I think she is beautiful!"

"But *all right*, Mom?"

"What do you mean?"
(How my self hated my mind for taking
to evasive flight when faced with the unthinkable!)

"I thought she was all right until today when Martha
came with her baby, and they're so different!
And they shouldn't be, for they were born the same week.
My baby doesn't smile, reach out and touch things,
coo, gurgle—or anything!
She doesn't respond at all!"

Naomi began to cry, but she wept like a beginner
to grief. Hers was the dazed, bewildered, puzzled lamentation
of one whose joy has fled temporarily,
like the sun in a blue sky
sliding under a random dark cloud.

And I, the mother who gave her birth,
I, who knew that Naomi's world was beginning to unravel,
tried to knit it together with a lie.

"But no babies are ever the same!
Any pediatrician will tell you that no infant
develops just like another one!"

Consoled by my lie, Naomi went back to her room
and left me with my birds, dipping wing-wind close.
But now fists of self-torment
rose out of the batwind and struck at me.

Why, oh, why, are we so often helpless
when dear ones cry for help?
Why do we falter and fail
and leave them in the lurch
just then,

just when the situation cries out:
"Here is the come-at-able,
get-at-able, reachable moment.
The door is ajar,
the way is unclogged.
Be true!
Be true!"

I lay with closed eyes,
but the flames of Naomi's burning Eden
flickered on the screen of my eyelids.
Quench, quench the fire!
Where was the water to quench that fire?
A bucket brigade of scraps of Bible verses
marched through my mind.

He hath torn, and he will heal. . . .
Cast all your cares. . .
The oil of joy for mourning. . .
The garment of praise for the spirit of heaviness. . .

But they were no water,
only the dust of empty promises.
Indeed, casting them on the fire
seemed to make the flames spit and spurt higher.

Words with the weight of authority
and the ring of command trooped into my mind:

Is there any one among you suffering?
Let him pray.

Obediently I tried to pray, but all that came
was a clutter of agitated words and phrases,
all of them beseeching healing for Nani, help for Naomi:

"For the sake of Nani,
for the sake of Naomi,
God, please help!
Please help!"

Not until the drab of a relapsed-to-winter dawn
did I realize that it was my own Eden—not Naomi's—
that was burning.
My own insouciant and secure but false paradise
was being cremated, and the fuel of the flame
constituted "the precious words of comfort,"
"the sacred words of consolation"
I had accumulated in my lifetime in the church.
But the promissory notes were not being paid on demand!
Were they false? Was the deity I was addressing
a paper God, as powerless as a fairy godmother?
Suddenly I felt as silly as the Old Woman
standing frustrated and helpless with the pig
that refused to go over the stile, and crying:

"Rope, rope, hang butcher
Butcher, butcher, kill ox
Ox, ox, drink water,
Water, water, quench fire
Fire, fire burn stick
Stick, stick, beat dog
Dog, dog, bite pig

Pig won't go over the stile
and I won't get home tonight."

Could I, would I, ever go home again
to that paradise of pious promises?

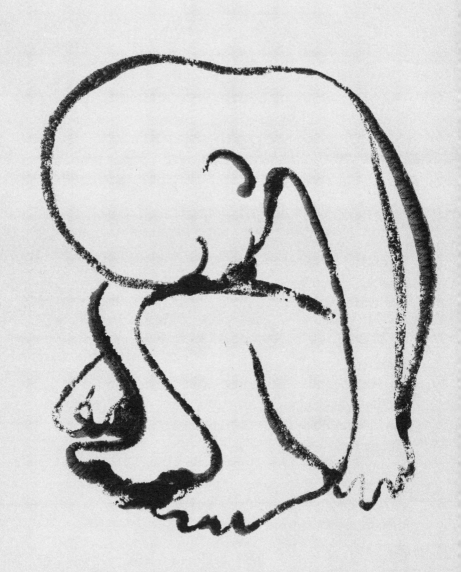

Until the first of May, when Naomi
flew with her baby back to the island paradise
that was now her home,
she and I separately and secretly searched
for signs that whispered hope.
Alone with Nani, I rallied
and distilled all my natural resources of tenderness
and love and sought in vain for a funnel hole
through which to pour this quintessence
into her opacity.
I even played the clown
in trying to evoke a flicker smile.
Indeed, I even impersonated
a character I despise—

the babbling, gushing, cooing, clucking,
chin-chucking magpie-grandma—
but to no avail.
There was no open sesame.
My natural, bred-in-the-bone hope snapped
and broke.

But Naomi's native, ingrained hope,
a greener stick than mine,
drank the sap of youth and tilted upward again,
especially when Martha left with her baby
and like and unlike
no longer cruelly confronted each other.
Naomi flew home on the wings of the instinctive
optimism of the very young.

All is ill and very ill
but all will be well again.
Time will heal,
time will mend.
All will be well again!

In the very young, hope is yeast
and hope is east, a habit
like the rising sun.
But Naomi was flying west in more ways than one,
and I trembled to think of the sunset
of her immediate, spontaneous hope.

"We're going to take Nani to the best specialist
in Hawaii," were her parting words.

The medical reports Naomi included in her letters
over the next two years were progressively worse.

"Nani is in a cast.
The doctor found that she has something
congenitally wrong with her hip."

"The doctor is testing her hearing.
There seems to be something wrong with it.
Maybe that's why she doesn't respond.
But don't worry, Mom and Dad,
a lot can be done with a deaf child."

When the seizures began, Naomi panicked
and made frequent calls.

"They're awful," she sobbed from halfway around the world.
"I can't stand to watch her have them."

The seizures were controlled by medication,
and the testing went on.
The final report also came in a telephone call,
in a dull dead voice:
"The doctors say that Nani
had severe brain damage before birth.
She is deaf and untrainable.
She probably will never have more mentality
than a three-month-old baby.
The doctor thinks that she
should be put in an institution.
A place like Barrington, Mom! Barrington!"

27

The receiver crackled with her wild weeping,
and this was the weeping of one
who had begun at the beginning
and had come a long way into grief.

After a long time:
"Mom, are you still there?"

"Yes, oh, yes! I'm crying with you!"

"What shall we do? What shall we do?"

You hope and hope and hope
and then you do not hope anymore.
Hope goes out.
All hope goes out
and you do not hope anymore.

Nani, Nani, my pretty one!
Every test has subtracted from you.
Almost everything human has been taken from you—
hearing, talking, walking, feeling,
discovering, learning.
What remains?
Nothing but just being—
just subsisting?
What kind of subsisting being,
Nani, are you?

Seeking an answer to my question, I drove to Barrington

and wandered about among the sights, sounds,
and smells of a state institution.

The mongoloids,
the severely retarded,
the physically and mentally abnormal—
all these defective specimens of humanity
who gibber meaninglessly,
slobber incessantly,
rock monotonously,
grab, and gesticulate senselessly
or just lie inertly,
who often stink in spite of frequent washing
and whom we shut away and out of our sight.

On the way home and all that night
I turned my despair and rage upon the Creator.
I taunted him.
I threw my beautiful blighted grandchild
and the whole menagerie
of grimacing deformities and monstrosities
into his face.

What are you—Creator or Father?
If Creator,
are *they* your image?
Do *you,* then, have a monster head?
Are *you* hunchbacked, clubfooted?
Do we worship a Divine Freak?
Do we pray to a Divine Absurdity,
a Supernatural Monster?

If Father,
then what happened to all the fatherly
virtues: tenderness, protectiveness,
affection, solicitude?

Answer me, you who claim to be
both Creator and Father.
Answer!

But all I got was silence.
I scolded him like a shrew.
I displayed the temper of a female fiend.
I insulted him.
I poured out obscenities
I did not know I had within me.

But he was silent,
and I remembered a verse in a psalm and found it:

"Is he deaf, the God who planted the ear?"

And if I, thousands of space miles removed
from the source of pain,
I who could never know or feel the fullness
of pain that Nani fountained,
if *I* was hurling my rage and despair
at the Divine Tormentor,
what were Nani's parents doing, saying, thinking?
Were they who leaned over the crib
of their perennial infant
praying the ageless petition:

Remove thy stroke from me;
I am spent by the blows of thy hand?

33

Were they piteously pleading for
a "Take up thy bed and walk" miracle?
Were they comparing their misfortunate selves
with the fortunate?

For they have no pangs;
their bodies are sound and sleek.
For they are not in trouble as other men are;
they are not stricken like other men.

Were they hurling men's eternal,
agonized "Why?" at heaven?

Why did you do it?
Why did you give our baby life
and then take away everything
that makes life worth living?
Explain yourself!
Justify yourself!

Where had I read it?
Was it Edna St. Vincent Millay?
"Distressed mind,
Forbear to tease the hooded why.
The shape will not reply."

Were Nani's parents, too, meeting
only a vast silence?
And was it the silence of a cosmic,
infinite embarrassment?

Why are you silent, Creator God?
Are you in such a pickle,
you who keep your rod in pickle,
that you cannot answer?
Would you rather not own up to being
the Author of such an inhuman mess
as the human mess you have created?
We are not complaining of our man-made mess
but of yours:
the maiming and the paining
of the innocents.
And if you did not create the sufferings
of the innocent, why do you consent
to all that happens
and how?

And you, Savior, Mediator, Intercessor,
the Lamb of God, the Man of Sorrows,
Son of God and Son of Man,
why are *you* silent?
Have you forgotten what it means to be man,
the giant agony of being man,
and therefore you are silent?
Or are you silent
because you remember so well?

And you, the most neglected member of the Trinity,
you, the Holy Spirit, the Dove, the Comforter,
the Consoler, the Counselor—
why are *you* silent?

Has the job of consoling the unconsolable
become so depressing and so dis-spiriting
that you have closed your practice?

O Divine Indifference,
we cry out for sounds that mean something.
Words, real words, authentic words!
Not the pat, fat phrases of the mealymouthed pious,
not "devotional helps"
"lessons for life learned from life"
"peace of mind" platitudes.
(Those whose pain has no exit
are forever exiled from "peace of mind"!)

Words, real words!
Not new scientific psychological dogmas
(by now we know that newness
does not spell success,
and the patients get no better).

Words, real words!
Not the existentialists' counsel
of brave despair: "Life is ultimate
tragedy, ha, ha! But have the courage
to be." (How does one *get* that courage
to be?)

Where were the words to come from
when no springs spurted from God's unspeakingness,
science's helplessness,

the intellectuals' hopelessness?
We might as well talk to a rock about our grief!

Yet there had to be real words.
Youthful optimism had toppled,
buoyant spontaneous hope had had its deathblow,
and I knew, I knew in the innermost
depths of my being
the exhaustion, the paralysis, the despair
in the wake of such a loss.
But I also knew now as never before
that the words could not come from me.
I had no answers.
No tranquilizers for mental distress on my shelves.
No tonics for despondency.
No antidotes for the poison of suffering.
No wealth of wisdom for the bankruptcy of spontaneous,
immediate hope.
No clues to the paindom!

If we, Naomi's parents, could not say anything
to alter our daughter's anguish over her firstborn,
could we perhaps *do* something?

"Should *you* go to her or should I?" I asked her father.
"Or should we bring her and the baby home for a time?"

Something within us said, "No."
In those very hours and days and weeks
when we were most anxious and concerned about Naomi,

when we yearned to take her in our arms
and speak to her pain all the tender,
compassionate, loving words we knew,
something told us to keep the distance
of an ocean between us.

And this is how I began to realize that God
is perhaps more concerned when he is silent,
when he seems to have stepped aside or withdrawn,
than at any other time!
This is how I began to discern, to my bitter shame,
the unworthiness and the obtuseness of calling
divine silence the death of God—
to say nothing of my browbeating my God!
I had not mocked God;
I had mocked myself.
I had not harmed God;
I had harmed myself.

In such a mood, I discovered words,
real words, words so real that they came
with the effect of a bomb
rather than of a bromide.
Strangely enough, Psalm 73 addressed itself
to *me* and not to Naomi!

When my soul was embittered,
when I was pricked in heart,
I was stupid and ignorant,
I was like a beast toward thee.

Nevertheless I am continually with thee;
thou dost hold my right hand.
Whom have I in heaven but thee?
My flesh and my heart may fail,
but God is the strength of my heart
and my portion for ever.

For two years Nani's parents shifted
between two poles: joy and pain.
Joy with its hope of the possible.
Perhaps.
Maybe.
There may be a chance.
It is possible.
God willing.
Pain with its consciousness of the impossible.
No hope at all.
No chance whatsoever.
It is hopeless.
It is impossible.
God is not willing.

Gradually the burden of proof
and the weight of evidence
shifted to the pain pole.
The unthinkable was not only thinkable,
it was undeniable, unmistakable.
There was no hope.

Shortly before the scales tipped
irrevocably to the impossible,
Naomi wrote a letter which indicated
that she was fully aware that this was coming.
It was stream-of-consciousness writing—
the consciousness rushing down
mind-mountains and mind-cliffs
to the ocean of inevitability.

"We want to keep Nani so much—
oh, we love her more and more—
we don't know what will happen—it's strange—
I've never really had the thought before—
I know it's useless upsetting ourselves—
but what will happen to Nani
when she is as old as we are now?
She is so beautiful and healthy—
but completely helpless.
I think it's our hopes that hurt the most—
or maybe the fears—
I can't imagine what it is like to be her—
can she think?
We don't know what to do—

oh, I can't do it!
Oh, I know I can!
I don't think like this all the time.
It kills me when I do!"

It was the last sentence which chilled me.
"I don't think like this all the time.
It kills me when I do."

Naomi cannot, she must not, be "killed."
It was not the fear of physical death which haunted me,
for Naomi had demonstrated several times
that her life instinct was imperious.
It was the suffocating and the killing
of her spirit that I feared,
the slow strangling when a stone,
an irreducible something,
is planted in the soul,
and the spirit can no longer breathe freely and deeply.
The breath of the spirit becomes more and more shallow—
until there is no perceptible breath,
and the spirit is as if dead.

Pain resisted could be this killer, this stone.
It could be even more;
it could be a foreign malignant body
that not only lies there in the soul
inert and irreducible
but also exudes the suffocating carbon dioxide
of despondency, defiance, and despair.

Pain resisted could intensify, worsen the pain.
Any woman who has given birth
knows the consequences of stiffening her body
against the contractions of the uterus
in its uncompromising will to deliver its freight.
Birth pangs resisted give no quarter, become
ruthless and relentless.
If the body's resistance is as relentless
and ruthless as the uterus' determination to give birth,
the body may have to submit to Caesarean incision.
If it will not assent to the pain of birth,
it will have to assent to a wound.

But in and of itself pain is a wound;
indeed, all creation seems to bear the wound of pain.
As the old adage goes, "Man is born
in another's pain and perishes in his own."
Pain lies at the center of existence
in the same way as Nani is the nucleus of pain
in her parents' daily life.

The mystery of Nani!
Would it be necessary to go through the dark
valley of Nani to find the mystery of pain and suffering?
And if all of us who loved Nani
did not learn the mystery, were we doomed
to learn bitterness, tension, depression,
resentment, meaninglessness?

Do suffering and pain have a formula?
And the solution to suffering, too?

44

Suffering$=A^2 + 3\,ab + b^4$?
Solution to Suffering$=X^5 - 3(x - 2y) - 4y^2$?

If I could master the mathematics of pain,
if I could learn the alphabet of suffering,
could I, if necessary, help my daughter
to creep again,
to walk again,
or even to fly again—
in the spirit?

But how can one work out
equations (or a gospel) for suffering
when there are so few givens,
and the givens are all negative?
And were they really givens,
or my personal, private intuitions, based mainly on fear
that Naomi, who had stumbled into a path of suffering,
unchosen and inescapable,
would in time reach the limit of her endurance
and would travel some descending path?
My only positive intuition—
certainly not a given—
was that suffering is cloaked in mystery
and yet has a mystery to reveal.
If Naomi did not learn this mystery,
her spirit might be killed.
Could I, her mother, unravel the mystery?
Could I find a daybreak that could become
another's dawning?

They could have been contemporaries—
the Greek poet Homer,
the Hebrew poet David,
and the unknown Hebrew who met the problem
of the suffering of the innocent
head-on in the Book of Job.

Enticed by the glamor of the less familiar,
I steered my quest for a solution to suffering
first to the Greek pagan mind.
The year 1000 B.C. was a different age from ours,
but I soon discovered that the essential
problem of living was the same,
its pain was the same,
and its tears were the same.

In the first and greatest of antiquity's
pagan poets I heard the universal lament
of the bereaved mother
in the cry of Hector's mother:

My child,
Ah, woe is me!
Wherefore should I live in my pain,
Now that thou art dead. . . ?

The world of man was very young in 1000 B.C.,
but the shadow of impending catastrophe
hung over life even then.
Achilles said as much
to the father of the dead Hector:
This is the lot the gods
have spun for miserable men,
that they should live in pain,
yet themselves are without sorrow.

"Reckon no man happy," said Creon
in *Oedipus the King*, "until you witness
the closing day, until he passes the border
which severs life from death,
unscathed by sorrow."

The ancient Greeks knew the existential fact
of human suffering.
But a solution to suffering?

I read the epics, the tragedies,
the comedies (which were never far from tears),
but I found no equations.
Helpless victims of fate are defenseless
and formulate no formulas.
Nevertheless—
and the glory of Homer and of the Greeks
is in that one word *nevertheless*—
they accepted life as a glorious adventure
and lived it so.
Face to face with the mystery of death,
often sudden and violent death,
they lived the mystery of joyous life.
They seemed to find goodness
even in the taste of the salt of tears!

As I read on in ancient Greek literature
I saw the dawn of the idea
that the seeds of self-destruction, of pain and suffering,
are in the interior of man.
By the time the great Greek tragedians
began writing (500-400 B.C.) the Greeks had developed
the concept of *hybris*,
the sin of pride,
that man by his own insolence and impudence can
call down the punitive wrath of the gods
and thus be responsible for capsizing his own ship of life.
But not even Socrates understood that the dark passions
which create havoc and suffering on the human scene
are so deeply ingrained that they cannot be eradicated

by knowledge, by sweetness and light!
Not even you, Socrates, noblest of the pagans,
had a radical solution!

Still bypassing the Hebrew desert poets,
David, and the poet of Job,
I searched the pagan mind
farther and farther to the East.
Admittedly I scratched only the surface of literature,
but wherever I scratched
I found an underlying human scene as modern as today.
I found the earth saturated with human tears,
"soaked from its crust to its core,"
as Ivan said in *The Brothers Karamazov.*
Often I found the dim dawning of the idea
that the human personality is a paradoxical thing
for which no formula can be found.
In the Persian epic *Firdausi,*
Rustem, the unwitting slayer of his own son, Sohrab,
saw himself as the "spring of all this scene of woe."
Some few of the ancient pagan minds perceived
that there is nothing fixed and tangible in man,
either in his mind or his nature,
that lends itself to a human equation
that will solve his own dilemma.

In the literature of the Far East, however,
I found very conscious efforts
to create a formula for suffering.
Indeed, the religions of the Far East
were structured as simple equations:

Solution to Suffering=Indifference

Indifference to pleasure as well as to pain.
Indifference to gain as well as to loss,
to victory as well as to defeat.
Desire nothing for oneself,
for all that the senses desire is nothing.
But in and of itself the solution,
the equation, the religion
was a shrinking in pain
from the spectacle of human pain!
It was no solution at all,
for it created an even greater paradox
in the human personality
and engaged man in an utterly self-centered
and selfish striving to be selfless.

The mind of the Far East may still cry:
I know the answer to pain.
I have found it.
It is to be indifferent.
But its painfully cultivated indifference
is nothing more than a shriek of pain,
muffled and stifled!
Its claim to a solution merely affirms
its solidarity with all human suffering!

With dragging feet,
like an adolescent finally but
reluctantly turning to old parents
to find the wisdom he has hopefully
and vainly sought elsewhere,
I turned to the Old Testament.
I came prepared to find suffering
but not to discover that the entire
Old Testament is an epic of a suffering nation,
that in some ways the name "Israel"
is synonymous with suffering.
I was prepared to find circumstances
of particular suffering.
David's heartrending cry at the death
of his traitor son will always ring in my ears:

O my son Absalom,
My son, my son Absalom!
Would I had died instead of you,
O Absalom, my son, my son!

But I was not prepared to find again and again
the figure of the Suffering Servant
who takes upon himself the full weight
of man's ephemeral and afflicted life.

I was prepared for pious platitudes
and practical prudence
on the subject of suffering,
and Proverbs for the most part
bore out my expectations:

The fear of the Lord prolongs life
but the years of the wicked will be short.

The righteous is delivered from trouble
and the wicked gets into it instead.

No ill befalls the righteous,
but the wicked are filled with trouble.

I was even prepared for the psalmists'
bewilderment and resentment that their simple
equations did not seem to work out in actuality.
Righteousness did not always equal
success, prosperity, felicity, and bliss.

Unrighteousness did not always equal
failure, adversity, sorrow, and tribulation.
I was prepared to hear the psalmists cry out,
"It isn't fair! It isn't fair!"
and so they did.
But I was totally unprepared for the fury
of the Hebrews' anger against wickedness and for the depth
of their own grief and penitence when they found themselves
to be guilty of wickedness.
In the pagan literature I had found
lasciviousness and cold cruelties
pretty much taken for granted,
but not here in the Old Testament!
Here the righteous man almost seemed to luxuriate
in his hatred of unrighteousness.
Was the pagan's tolerance due to his belief in gods
who were themselves lascivious
and prone to fits of petulant cruelty?
Did the Hebrew's hatred of sin flow from his God,
who was implacably hostile to sin
but at the same time utterly concerned for the sinner?
So concerned, in fact, that he seemed
to have his own private hell of pain and suffering,
and it was his love for man!
He cared enough for man to place within him
an infinite goal of perfection,
to stand in judgment upon his failure
to strive toward that goal,
to discipline and punish him for rebelling
against that infinite goal.

Yet all the time he was acting in his father role
of "bringing up the children"
he experienced the father-agony of seeing his children
go astray and writhe in their own self-made torments.
Truly there was no god like this God,
the God of the Hebrews, this God
who was at one with his children
despite their rebellion, despite their affliction!
It was almost as if I, a spiritual adolescent,
had to see and to scrutinize other parents, other gods,
before I realized the superiority
of my own parent, my own God!

But still not a word to unravel the riddle of suffering!
Still no clues to Nani! I had found
various modes of living in the face of suffering.
The Greek pagan walked boldly
on the thin thread of life the Fates spun,
and if it was cut and he was hurled into the abyss,
he fell without whimpering.
The Eastern pagan contemplated away
his pain along with his pleasure
and dreamed of a better reincarnation
and the ultimate bliss of perfect peace—
the end of a life of self-conscious being
and absorption into the Absolute.
As for the Hebrew, whatever his suffering condition—
as a slave, deportee, or refugee
(and he was almost always one of these!)—
he *exulted* in his God.

He exulted even in his God's severe Law
and in his God's constant searching out
the secret depths of man's soul.

It took centuries of cudgeling to hammer
into the Hebrew skull the idea that pleasure and prosperity
are *not* God's reward for righteousness,
nor are pain and affliction his punishment
for unrighteousness.
The Book of Job, that most splendid creation
of Hebrew poetry, toppled that naive notion
once and for all in its message
that God is a transcendent God
whose ways are past finding out
and whose purposes are inscrutable.
God is God, and he is to be served for love
and not for reward.
Yes, one *exults in him* in the midst of deepest affliction
of body, mind, and spirit—
in deepest despair.

Job had to descend to the lowest depths of despair
to explode the rosy moral equation
which identified happiness and prosperity
with righteousness and God's reward,
and pain and tribulation
with God's punishment.
His mind almost departed from sanity
when he contemplated how
from out of the city the dying groan,

and the soul of the wounded cries for help,
yet God pays no attention to their prayer.

But when his friends continued to cling
to their narrow view of suffering,
his mind broke through to a new view of human suffering
and of man's relationship to God.
If Job had sung a psalm after his breakthrough,
he would have sung:
Praise the Lord!
Praise the Lord, O my soul!
Praise him in loss.
Praise him in anguish.
Praise him in pain.
I will praise the Lord in every condition.
I will sing praises to the Lord as long as I live.
I will sing praises to my God while I have being.

And Job's psalm would have had a newness
that the psalms ascribed to David did not have.

But could Naomi sing this new psalm?
On the strength of Job's new wisdom,
could she sing her own psalm:
Praise the Lord.
Praise him for Nani.
Praise him for her damaged brain.
Praise him for her seizures.
Praise him for her deaf muteness.
The Lord is just in all his ways.
The Lord is kind in all his doings.

Poet of Job, you were wise,
the wisest of all the wisdom poets.
But suffering is still a paradox,
still the darkest and strangest of life's paradoxes:
And what comfort and consolation
is there in a paradox?

Leaving the Old Testament writers,
I stood at the door of the New Testament
but did not go in.
This time my reluctance was something
deeper than spiritual adolescence.
My mind told me it was because
the New Testament was all about
personal salvation and therefore could not
and would not illuminate
the problem of pain and suffering,
would supply no meaning for Nani,
no comfort for Naomi.
My heart told me that my notion was a pettifogging lie
and that my mind was evading and avoiding

the real reason for stalling
at the door of the New Testament
because the real reason would be incriminating.
My mind scoffed at the very idea.
How could a sincere, honest, old grandmother
diligently searching for a meaning
for her brain-damaged grandchild
possibly be incriminated?

But I did not go in.
I am ashamed to say that I not only leaped over
the New Testament, but over centuries
of Christian literature, including that
of Augustine, Dante, and John Bunyan.
My mind sprinted as fast as it could
to one whom it had met years before
and dimly remembered as having wrestled
with the enigma of innocent suffering—
namely, Ivan in *The Brothers Karamazov*.
Ivan was tormented by the same doubt
that tormented Job and was tormenting me.
How can one believe that a God who allows
even one innocent child to suffer
is a just God?
But where Job's faith floundered
on his own undeserved afflictions,
Ivan's faith and my own floundered
on the sufferings of children.
Less sure of our own innocence,
more doubtful of our own righteousness before God,
and more aware than Job of the odious and vicious

and diabolical self that coexists in our beings,
we could not take Job's self-righteous stance.
But we stood on sure ground for rebellion
when it came to the sufferings of children!
For me, Nani was reason enough to challenge a God
who gives a life but withholds everything
that makes life worth living.

" 'I say nothing of the sufferings of grown-up people,'
said Ivan to Alyosha,
'they have eaten the apple, damn them,
and the devil take them all. . . .
But these little ones? . . .
If all must suffer to pay for the eternal harmony,
what have children to do with it?
And if it is really true that they must share
responsibility for the father's crimes,
such a truth is not of this world
and is beyond my comprehension. . . .
I want to see with my own eyes
the hind lie down with the lion
and the victim rise up and embrace his murderer.
I want to be there when every one suddenly understands
what it has all been for.
All the religions of the world are built on this longing,
and I am a believer.
But then there are the children,
and what am I to do about them?
That's a question I can't answer.
For the hundredth time I repeat,

there are numbers of questions,
but I've only taken the children, because
in their case what I mean is so unanswerably clear. . . .
if the sufferings of children
go to swell the sum of sufferings
which was necessary to pay for truth,
then I protest that the truth is not worth such a price. . . .
And so I hasten to give back my entrance ticket. . . .
It's not God that I don't accept, Alyosha,
only I must respectfully return Him the ticket.' "

Had he not "handed in his ticket,"
Ivan would have been a nineteenth century Job.
By handing in his ticket, he retained
his intellectual integrity—
and lost his faith.

And I?
If I found no illumination, no meaning,
no equation for suffering,
the sufferings of the innocent,
would I, too, eventually hurl my entrance ticket
to the eternal harmony of eternity,
where there is no more suffering?
Would I hurl it into the face of
the Supernatural Monster who,
if he did not contrive it,
nevertheless *allowed* the existence
of this mortal disharmony?
Another Russian, Belinsky, had said that
"harmony itself is conditioned by disharmony.

This may be gratifying for lovers of music,
but it certainly is not for those who are doomed
to express disharmony in their own experience."

After reading and rereading Ivan's brilliant and profound
treatment of Job's question,
I was suddenly alarmed to discover that the quest
for a meaning for suffering to give my daughter
was taking a painful turn.
I had set my plowshare in the soil
of the world's great literature
and turned up human pain and human grieving,
but I was also turning up something else
that I did not wish to turn up.
The plowshare had turned inward
and was disturbing ground
that I did not wish disturbed.

Was it to prevent the uncovering
of humiliating contradictions
within my own self
that I suddenly decided to stop
looking in literature for the *meaning*
of pain and suffering
and looked instead for *reactions*
to pain and suffering?
Was it because I sensed the danger
of getting into something with all my being
that I stopped looking for something
about which I could say:
"Now I know it! I have found it!"
Was the cold objectifying method

of my next searching and summarizing
of reactions to pain
a frightened retreat from subjectivity?

Whatever the reason,
here are the somewhat chilly, compassionless
conclusions I drew up after reading,
night after night, this modern literature
which seems to have no god against whom
it can hurl its "why."
(Hence writers today are often not much more
than uninhibited and unembarrassed
gossipers of despair, purveyors
of the miseries and misfortunes of men.
Strangely enough,
the psychic suffering of man in literature
seemed to become more terrible
when he stopped asking "why"
and regarded pain and suffering
as utterly meaningless!)

But here is my outline of men's reactions to pain
in modern literature:

I. Evasion

A fugitive from pain, the "evader"
steers his life around all stresses and distresses,
keeps anguish at a distance, out of hearing.
By averting his eyes and holding his nose,
by plugging his ears

and shunning all entangling alliances,
he manages to avoid
every suggestion of the tragic
and develops the callous hide of a rhinoceros.
By pursuing pleasures rapaciously
(sensually, esthetically, and intellectually—
according to his temperament and gentility)
he does indeed evade the agonies of pain by day,
but his nights are stitched with pain
and preyed upon by bloodless shapes
as pale and inhuman as his own self.

II. Dilution

Time dilutes any pain that has an ending, but
the "diluter" hastens the watering-down process
with bracers, pills, and pick-me-ups and countless
clever compensations. He manufactures a silly,
sleazy optimism, flabby and soporific,
that mitigates the pain—or seems to. Or he
dilutes his pain by spreading it. He pouts
and piques and knifes and wounds. Every good
and beautiful thing is a personal insult and he
must smear it with his bitter bile.
Or he creates a compensatory Kingdom of God,
an artificial paradise,
the best of all possible artificial paradises,
where God-on-a-leash dispenses
success and happiness to those he favors,
failure and wretchedness to those he disfavors,
and consecrates every pain-palliative.

Determined to be happy, the "diluter"
dilutes his suffering with a mediocrity
which he finds insufferable!

III. Submersion

The "submerger" embraces his suffering, takes it
to bed with him at night, fondles and feels and
caresses it as if it were his favorite mistress.
The "submerger" gormandizes his afflictions,
tastes his pain and savors its unsavoriness,
smells the fragrance of its foulness. The
"submerger" listens to the throbbing of his
anguished heart, takes the temperature of his
misery hourly, measures his pain pressure, and
thrives on all the symptoms of his ills and griefs.

I still don't know why I attempted to catalog
and computerize men's reactions
to pain and suffering in modern literature:
all the way from the total collapse
of "I cannot endure it!"
to the jutting-jaw, self-willed tenacity of
"By God, I will endure it!"
I can only explain it now as the dodge of sophistry,
the dishonesty of speculating about
something one is beginning to experience himself
too painfully and keenly.
All the time I was savagely computerizing
men's inadequate reactions to human suffering,

I myself was guilty of one of the most common
of man's inadequate reactions and compensations!
Was it perhaps significant that the dodge
of sophistry about suffering
did not appear in my catalog?

Then within the space of twenty-four hours
two things happened that were totally
unexpected and implicit nudges
to do something I had not even
remotely considered.
Omitting all the "whens," "wheres," and "whys,"
I need only say that I encountered a woman
I had never seen before
and perhaps may never see again.
The encounter lasted but five minutes.

"At the countdown of 4," I told my Partner,
"we had taken care of the amenities.
By 3 we were conversing in depth.

At 1 she gave me a copy of
Herman Hesse's *Siddhartha,*
and at zero she rocketed off
and our orbits will probably never cross again."

In reading the book that night,
I was absorbed not by Siddhartha's lifelong
quest for truth
but by the *river,*
the river to which Siddhartha went,
wounded and disillusioned by life,
the river where he learned to know
love and serenity. Siddhartha loved
a river the way our family loves a river
in the wilderness of forest
along the Canadian border.
The strange woman with whom I had
spoken but five minutes
had given me a book about a seeker who
loved a river and listened to it,
listened "with a still heart
and a waiting, open soul,
without passion,
without desire,
without judgment,
without opinions."

The next day's mail brought
a new poem from a friend,
a native citizen of the Kingdom of Pain.

74

He was writing what he whimsically called psongs,
twelve line poems based on the psalms.
This one had flowed out of Psalm 42:

"As a deer thirsts for running streams,
so my soul longs for You, O God.
My tears have been my only food;
men taunt me with 'Where is your God?'
God, my soul is in agony.
Ocean deeps call to ocean deeps
in the roar of Your waterfall.
All of Your waves break in my soul!
Why are you in despair, my soul,
Why do you know such turbulence?
Wait for God! Hope expectantly,
for I shall yet praise Him for help!"

Again it was not the despairing soul, the soul in agony,
that dispossessed all other thoughts,
but the "running streams,"
the "roar of your waterfall."
And the "Wait for God: Hope expectantly:
For I shall yet praise Him for help:"

The strange coincidence of the gift
of the book and the poem . . . all in the same day,
created an overwhelming longing for our Northwoods river,
and the feeling quickly became
a compulsion, a necessity, an urgency.
The nudging had become so strong that I actually felt

rib-sore, just as one feels tension in knotted
stomach muscles and fear in cold, goose-fleshed skin.
My Partner, who understands me better, I sometimes feel,
than I do myself, let me go by myself immediately
to be alone with the river.

Siddhartha came to his river
with the wound of a meaningless life. I came to my river
with the wound of a beloved child's meaningless suffering.
Siddhartha lived out his lifetime on his river and found
his truth. I hoped to find my meaning
on my river in the single month of June.

It was this sense of urgent expectancy
which nearly frustrated the whole effort.

In the first place, I saw Naomi everywhere
on the river which she loved as much as I do.
I could see her swimming across the rapids
to the huge safe boulders on the other side
for the first time—her eyes wide and wild
with an admixture of fear, hope, trust, and joy.
I could see her draped on one of the huge
sun-warmed boulders in the middle of the river,
reading happy-ending novels
and weeping quietly when one happened not to end that way.
Over the years the boulders had acquired names:
The Chair, The Couch, The Table, The Throne,
The Saddle, The Giantess Lap, Gog and Magog,
and each time I passed them, I saw her slim tanned body
molded to one or another.

In the second place, whether I was in or on the river
my mind kept making metaphors and creating parables
out of every sight, sound, and sensation I experienced.
For example, the mosquitoes and migs
in the north woods in June are wicked demolishers
of contemplation, but a spraying of insect repellent
held them a few comfortable insect-lengths away.

"Aha!" said my adumbrating mind.
"We humans hold off pain and suffering just like that.
A throb of pain—take an aspirin or Novocain.
A droning of depression—take a tranquillizer.
A hint of tiredness—take a pep pill."

When, after lying prone on the Table boulder for an hour,
watching the skater-bugs glide fluently
among the foam bubbles in the amber water,
I discovered that the skater bugs
cast a shadow of four balanced plump dots
around a center—and that foam bubbles cast hardly a shadow,
my hounddog mind bayed excitedly.

I have a little shadow
that goes in and out with me
and what can be the use of him
is more than I can see.

Pain is man's shadow—
and only things with substance
cast a shadow.

Nonentities are not vested
with shadow.
Can pain then be meaningless?
Hollow men do not suffer
as much pain as whole men.
Do hollow men
cast a shadow?

When my feet rediscovered the hidden but safe
bracing rocks at the foot of the waterfall
and I leaned into the surging, buffeting,
battering cascade until my reddened body was dissenting
but exhilarated, once again my mind went to work
turning this, too, into grist for its gist-mill.

The fussy little dictator on his bone-throne in my cranium
did not surrender until I spent my entire day
totally concentrated, physically and mentally,
on making a path along the river
to an otherwise inaccessible beautiful gorge and waterfall.
That night I fell into bed exhausted,
slept a dreamless sleep, and woke to a mind
that was no longer conceiving parables for its own gospel,
nor dictating its own answers.

The next day June reverted
to April's cloudiness and coolness.
On any other day I would have stoked
the wood range with big chunks of birch,
built a fire in the fireplace,
and read all day in cabin comfort,
but reading would only make
my mind talkative again. Our family had already
discovered that on such a day
swimming in the river is not only tolerable
but utterly pleasurable if wedded to a sauna.
So I had my day on the river anyway,
alternately roasting in tropical heat
on the top shelf of the sauna

and swimming in the frigid water of the river.
The warmth lingered long in the sauna
after the fire subsided, and I lay on my stomach
looking out the window at the river foaming
and cascading through the deep cleft
it had made in the black basalt rock
spring-torrents ago. Or I closed my eyes
and listened to the sound which anywhere else
but here would have terrified me,
for it was not unlike the roaring when a violent
Midwest storm breaks the dull, stupid torpor
of a hot and humid summer day.
Here on the river the sound was pure Beethoven.
I fell asleep sauna-warm and naked,
and awoke chilled and feeling that the afternoon
was fast sliding toward night.

It was not until I had climbed the cliff path
to the cabin and the teakettle was singing
and the coffeepot perking
that I was aware that something had happened.
I had floated free from a distorted
and distorting mood and was existentially
moving toward a new happening,
a new "awaring."
My mind had first assaulted heaven
with rage and despair over Nani
and then had frantically and frenetically
labored to find a meaning that would encompass
and explain her suffering and all suffering,

voluntary and involuntary.
Now my mind had finally been brought to a standstill,
and a profound change seemed to be taking place
between myself and the mystery of the suffering.

Was this standstill perhaps necessary?
Does one have to stand and wait patiently
on the border of a new continent of awareness—
wait for a visa to enter?
Does one have to be stripped and searched there
and divested of every perception, preconception,
prejudice, and mood that could be alien coin
in this new country?
Socrates had had to stand still to come to himself.

Gunnar Myrdal in his preface to *Asian Drama* wrote:
"When men have learned not to be frustrated because
their wishes are not immediately fulfilled
and not to be bitter because the world
has proved tougher and more complex than they had dreamed,
then they may be in a mood to value truth very highly."

My anger, bitterness, and despair had vanished.
As yet my truth, my meaning, was imperceptible—
not even a hint on the distant mindscape—
but the barrier to it was gone.
It was a humbling experience. I realized that
what I, with my little sprinkling of adversities,
had come slap up against was *not*, as I had thought,
the wall of the pain and suffering of my daughter Naomi

83

over her firstborn child, but the wall of my own
interior jungle. My daughter's pain had entered my being
and broken its apparently sweet harmony.
The dissonance of my jungle,
which had always been there in *pianissimo,*
had become pandemonium *fortissimo,*
and now all was quiet.
But not the same quiet as before!
Moreover, the barriers to the new awareness,
whatever it would be, were down.

What about Naomi, living
at the agonizing center, the pivotal point of pain,
and experiencing what I felt only at its edge?
Was she also moving out of dazed pandemonium
toward a new happening, a new awaring?
Had her mind, too, ceased to demand
divine apologies and explanations
and become silent?

In my own silence there in the cabin
I knew that Naomi's could be another kind of silence.
It could be a locking of the grief and pain
in the unconscious, a trying to be happy
by not thinking about it.
But any one-headed creature of our interior jungle
we relegate to the silence of the unconsciousness
emerges in unexpected places and at unexpected
times with two or three heads,
and the dissonance is augmented
by that many more mouths to shriek.

Thus Naomi, brought to a standstill by pain and suffering,
and I, her mother, brought to a standstill
by her pain and suffering,
stood at the border of two continents:
one that transcended self-pity, depression and despair
and brought a new relationship to the suffering;
and one, a subcontinent,
where demons sucked at the grief,
fed upon the suffering,
and begot a progeny of baleful brats.

There was little sleep for me that night,
for my mind suddenly was released
from the request to be silent
and carried on a lively dialogue with thoughts
that were not my own—
at least they came out of the night
like virgins with brightly-trimmed lights.
For a while as I lay wide awake watching
the stars and planets slide across
the cabin window that looked down the river,
I felt as if these thoughts and I
were about to make a landing on this new
continent to which the stillness had brought me,
but gradually it became clear

that it was the subcontinent
we were to visit this night,
the subcontinent of "No,"
the Fatherland of Negation,
inhabited by No-men who live there
by chance or by choice.

If Naomi were to settle down
in this gray No-man's land,
it would be by chance, by sliding toward it
in an ambiguous sort of way
when the downweight of existential life
proved to be greater than
the uplift of her youthful life forces.
When the bright expectations of youth went out,
one by one, as they inevitably do
(and this blackish grief of hers
could hasten the inevitability)
she *could* find herself an unwilling
but permanent resident of this subcontinent.
For Naomi, as it has been for countless others,
it would be a *descent*
from the Kingdom of the First Spontaneity
to the gray coasts of Null.

"How does it really happen?"
my mind asked its virgin visitors,
and the brightest of them answered:

Almost imperceptibly for those who inhabit
the Kingdom of the First Spontaneity long past

its season. There is enough vital fluid in
youthful first spontaneity to take care of
the April showers which into each life must fall.

And God is good and God is love
and God is in his heaven
and all is right with the world.

When surprised by large griefs and astonished
by sinister afflictions, the young invent
fictions to think themselves happy.

And God is still good and God is love
and God is in his heaven
and all is right with the world.

When their buoyant hopes of being beautiful people
and living beautiful lives in a beautiful world
are grounded, they modify their lives
to soften the bitterness.

And God is still good and God is love
and God is in his heaven
and all is right with the world.

They structure their lives to avoid
the sights and sounds and smells of suffering
and know not true suffering but only the frustration
of their attempts to structure their lives to avoid
the sights and sounds and smells of suffering.

89

And God is still good and God is still love
and God is still in his heaven
and all is still right with the world.

They bypass all the possibilities which menace existence—
the possibility of unhappiness
the possibility of despair
the possibility of offense—
and in the end this proves to be the greatest menace of all
and causes their downfalling to the subcontinent of No,
for they never learn to their utter astonishment
that they are not what they imagine themselves to be.
Indeed, they are nothing, their happiness is nothing,
their security is nothing, and their God and their
heaven are the most fraudulent fiction.
For never to move out of
the Kingdom of the First Spontaneity
is to become an involuntary No-man
and to descend to the subcontinent of No.
To fortify this kingdom against the mortal combat
between Yes and No in this world,
against the pain and suffering of that combat,
is to descend to the subcontinent of No.
To refuse to join the struggle
between the forces of Yes and No in this world,
to say No to the struggle,
is to descend to the subcontinent of No.
In a way they can be said to be April-fooled
into the subcontinent,
and yet it is not entirely innocent, their descending.
Perhaps it is more correct to say that they are not

90

there by choice but by reason of a thousand little
choices outly and not inly prompted.

But some have *elected* this subcontinent of No,
have voted No to the Yes
Yes to the No.
Confronted with the stark truths of life—
Dauchau, Lidice, Hiroshima, Vietnam, Nigeria,
leukemia, Parkinson's disease, meaninglessness,
death ("Man is being-toward-death," they say)—
they surrender to hopelessness and despair,
call existence absurd, and write bitter
comedies about it.

"Yes, oh yes!" I interrupted excitedly.
"I read something like that in Kierkegaard's *Journals*
not long ago and wrote it into my own journal."
I lit a candle, found the notebook, and
so strong was my feeling of carrying on a dialog
with the virgin thoughts that I read it aloud.

" 'All is phony, so let us laugh. Everything is lousy,
so let us clink the glasses. . . .'
What an abyss of perdition!
At the bottom of it all lies despair.
To want to do even the least bit
to halt this demoralization . . .
this they would regard as ridiculous.
'Let it hit bottom!' And although we sink in it,
we entertain ourselves with witty comedies
which expose the perdition.

91

'Done for,' they say. 'We are done for.
Nobody should complain about anybody. So let's all
laugh—the crazier the better.
Let's not only be wretched—
let's refine it with cleverness and wit
and dramatize it brilliantly.' "

And it was there in the candlelight
I found another note of Kierkegaard's
I had jotted down several years before
and forgotten completely:

"The ground and meaning of suffering:
dying to immediacy—
and that a man achieves nothing—
nothing at all by himself—
dying to immediacy
and remaining in finiteness."

There it was. Dying to the first immediacy.
Spiritual bankruptcy.
Choose now where you shall dwell:
Either in the subcontinent of No
Or in the continent of Yes!

This then is what suffering can and does do.
The mind that comes slap up against pain
also comes slap up against life's
most crucial Either/Or.

Washing clothes at the cabin is
an enchanting task. I place
the copper kettle on the wood range,
dipper amber river water into it,
cut thick slabs of yellow soap into it,
and immerse the soiled clothes.
When fragrant steam begins to rise
from the kettle, I leave my reading intermittently
to poke and turn the clothes with the handle
of a long wooden spoon. When the fire
has died down and the water cooled to lukewarm,
I wring out the clothes and carry them down
the cliff path to the river to rinse.

It was while I was sitting on my rinsing rock
that next morning, chin in hand,
anchoring a sheet against another rock
with my bare feet while it billowed
down the current and was flushed of suds,
that the idea of the "wound of grace" hit me.
Having been brought up on the concept of grace
as an oil, an herb, a balm, an unction,
the idea of grace as a wound was so astonishing
that I instinctively drew up my legs
and lost the sheet to the river.
But what is one old worn and mended sheet
to a fresh and brand-new concept?
The sheet would wrap itself around some
boulder far downstream and remain attached there
until it disintegrated,
whereas my new concept cut my mind loose
from an educated error
and set it free.

Coup de grace, a stroke of mercy,
was not an unfamiliar expression.
Moreover, I had seen it administered to a deer
struck by a speeding car but not killed outright.
But I had never applied the phrase
or heard it applied to men.

"I don't think like this all the time—
it kills me when I do," Naomi had written.
But maybe there had to be a "killing,"
a wound of grace!

The natural man, the creature of the first spontaneity,
does not choose pain and suffering.
Thus joy and happiness have come to be images of good,
of success, of blessing and benediction;
and pain and suffering have come to be images
of evil and of failure.
The God of grace seems always
to have been identified with progress and prosperity,
even in men's warfaring!
Only when the misfortune has an eventual
and favorable issue do we speak of
"a blessing in disguise."

Could men's spiritual retardation be due to this
correlation of happiness and success with God's grace,
and pain and failure with God's punishment?
Had I not witnessed with my own eyes
the sterility and banality of those
who in the eyes of the world
"enjoyed uninterrupted good fortune"?

"God can't be lived like some serenely shining morning,"
the poet Rilke wrote.
But men cling to the happiness and security
of earth's abundance
and refuse the wound of grace that will take them
far out and beyond immediacy,
giving them pain and insecurity,
perhaps even annihilating the "natural man."

97

To refuse the wound of grace may be
to refuse to be born again!
To be born again is to go through the pain
of dying to immediacy.

The creature of the first spontaneity conjugates his life
according to the laws of feeling and possibility:
I have felt happy.
I feel happy.
I will go on feeling happy.

I have felt secure.
I feel secure.
I will go on feeling secure.

In the face of minor frustrations
and fears and afflictions:
I have felt brave
I feel brave
I will go on feeling brave.

If he comes to a tougher, steeper uphill,
he grits his teeth, and, like the little red engine
in a child's story I had read many times to Naomi,
he thinks brave, stouthearted,
positive thoughts:
I think I can.
I think I can.
I think I can.

And maybe he can and maybe he does.
But then, too, he may never learn to know
his own true level of existence.
He may never be stripped of his illusions about life,
about others, about himself.
He may never be detached from his finite attachments
or disentangled from his transitory entanglements.
A larger reality may never
break into his present reality,
if the life he is living can in all tolerance
be called real.

In order to feel the fact of all
that is mortal and finite,
he who lives by feelings and on the strength
of finite possibilities
has to confront a dragon in his life—
the dragon of impossibility.
He needs to meet a situation where his brave little
humanly powered red engine disintegrates on the tracks
and with its last expiring breath pants:

I can't.
I can't!
It is impossible!

In other words, he needs the wound of grace
that makes him feel utterly unhappy,
utterly insecure,
utterly discouraged,
utterly helpless.

The bankruptcy of his feelings and possibilities,
the dissolution of his happy life of immediacy,
may by the grace of the wound turn into a becoming.
"Truth pierces matter where the heart is rent."

In my own salad days I had often secretly laughed
at Sunday school teachers and Sunday preachers
who prattled to my unreceptive ears,
"We must needs pass through death
that the old man may die."
It was Pauline theology, of course,
and not to my taste then.
It took years of chewing Paul
before I relished his taste.
But I suddenly realized there on the Rinsing Rock
that Paul was speaking out of his own experience
of a *coup de grace* on the Damascus road.
That expression "the old man,"
which had evoked nothing from me
in my youth but giggles,
meant the same as Kierkegaard's
"the creature of the first spontaneity,"
the first-nature man who wants to remain forever young,
forever happy, and forever secure in a world
where aging, death, despair, and insecurity
are built into the very fabric of life.
First-nature man cannot bear the weight
of such a world and must be annihilated—
by a wound of grace.

"Well, Paul, you fierce old Jew,"
I chuckled as I climbed the cliff path
with my laundry, minus one sheet,
"Your 2000-year-old theology explodes
again and again as the freshest news out,
and the fire-breathing dragon you met
on the Damascus road
turned out to be your Prince!"

That night timber wolves howled
on the ridge across the river
and were answered by wolves in the clearing
where the car was parked,
a dozen deer-leaps from the cabin door.
Wolf lovers insist that the timber wolf
is a beautiful and noble animal
and has his place in the Northwoods system.
Ignorance prevents me from joining the debate.
All I can say is that nothing shatters
one's illusion of his own courage
and drives fear into the marrowbone faster
than the nearby howling of timber wolves
on a dark and moonless night when one is

eight miles from another human being.
If the wolves had not been in the clearing,
I would have made an abject and craven
dash for the car
and not stopped for 300 miles
until I was safely at home with my Partner.
How utterly stupid to come
to the cabin without him!

I hooked the door, pushed the woodbox against it,
built up the fire in the fireplace,
and huddled by the hearth.
I gazed hypnotically into the fire,
not daring to look at the windows
lest I see there lewd, obscene eyes
spurting jets of flame.
I envisioned them leaping through the windows
and myself making my last stand
with my back to the fire, holding them off
for a while with a flaming broom,
but eventually falling to their slavering jaws.
The cabin would burn to the ground,
and the local newspaper would report that I had
perished in a cabin fire.
No one would ever know the nature
of my horrible death—no one!

If I survived the night, I would, of course,
go home at the first streak of dawn.

After carrying on a dialog for a half hour,
the wolves departed for other and distant ridges.
As fear drained out of me,
I was assailed by feelings of being a silly,
foolish old woman, full of egotism and illusions
about herself. Not only was I disillusioned with myself,
I was disillusioned with the headway
I thought I had been making
in understanding pain and suffering
and finding a meaning for Nani.
Even the buoyant, new concept that had cost a sheet
deflated in my mood of self-abnegation.

Was I to believe that Nani was a "wound of grace"
sent to wean Naomi from the sap of youthful spontaneity
before it inevitably dried up in the droughts and
deserts of existential life?
So that one person might have the possibility of becoming,
would God create another that could never become a self
even on the lowest level of consciousness?
If so, did this not mean that pain and suffering,
like the timber wolves, were part of a prescribed system;
that Nani's part in the system was similar
to that of the tender fawn destined for the wolf pack?

Did the God of grace use pain and suffering
to *torment* men into fruitful self-torment?
Was God, like Socrates and Kierkegaard,
scornful of the unexamined life, so scornful

that he bent and broke men on the rack
of pain and suffering
just to make contemplatives of them?
If so, what of the rank and file
who would bend and break
and never become contemplatives?
What was better—to rot in the unexamined life
or to bend and break under afflictions?
Did only philosophers and Einsteins inhabit
the kingdom?

Furthermore, if the purpose of pain and suffering
is to detach us from finite things
and train us for the life of the spirit in God,
then comfort and consolation are not only
inappropriate but downright detrimental!
Consolation which softens the bitterness
may prevent us from fleeing to God's grace.
Applying the salve of sympathy to the wound of grace
may seal up the opening through which grace may pass.
If this is true, then as far as spiritual life
is concerned, an ounce of non-intervention
might be worth a being-born-again
or a transition into the Second Spontaneity.
An ounce of compassion might mean the loss of the kingdom,
of the continent of Yes, and a descent to the non-kingdom,
the subcontinent of No.

Are all the laws in the kingdom,
that Yes-Continent of the spirit, *inverse?*

106

Is black white there?
Is up down and down up,
a loss gain and a gain loss,
pain a good and pleasure a harm,
a crushed and comfortless life good
and a pleasant and profitable life bad?

For two days my mind had been chafing and fretting
at the border of the continent of Yes
like Moses standing on the border of the Promised Land
and permitted only a glimpse of it.
I did not have forty years to spend in the wilderness!
With no evidence as yet to witness for the Yes-Continent
and all these subversive thoughts witnessing against it,
I wondered that night if I had not been led
down a dead end street,
if I had not been cruelly bamboozled or self-deluded.
Was what I had thought to be the testimony
of Spirit to my spirit
only the testimony of my heightened self?
What, if anything, did all this enlightenment
on the river have to do with my originally simple
desire to have a simple explanation
for innocent suffering?

What had begun as a dark night of terror
had turned into a dark night of the spirit.
I put another log on the fire and decided to spend
the rest of the night in a sleeping bag
on the floor before the fireplace.

107

"But even the dark night of the spirit
may be a form of grace,"
I whispered to myself much later,
and before I fell into deep sleep
I knew that it was indeed so.
I knew that these painful and confusing questions
were a gift of grace to my spirit,
sent to prevent there being anything maudlin,
namby-pamby, pedantic, smug, or even dogmatic
in my "simple explanation of innocent suffering."

Dawn sprouted in the dark soil of night,
unfurled its tendrils, and was day
in full flower before I awoke.
Instead of going home, I put a book
in a small backpack and took the path I had made
to the gorge down the river.
Fording the river at the end of my path,
where the cliff rose sheer and steep
a hundred feet or more,
I was able to enter the canyon
where the river began to fall in a series
of waterfalls. From the logs
and beaver-chewed chunks and driftwood
thrown high at the turn of the river,

111

one can see that at high-spring-flood time
the gorge is full of river.
Now, in the middle of a rather dry June,
I was able to wade through forking streams
and establish myself on dry bedrock
in the middle of the cascading waters
just above the largest waterfall.
I think I must have sat for a full hour feasting
on the festival banquet for all my senses—
the black cliff splashed with orange lichen,
the sun-warmed saddle of stone on which I sat,
the cool spray blown back on me
from the falls by an upstream breeze,
the aroma of balsam and spruce
growing on the high banks,
and the symphony of the river.

A span of but twelve hours between
a state of fear and trembling
and a state of inebriate rapture!
Now I was in no mood to search out
a gospel of suffering in the book
I had brought to the gorge.
But, obedient to my pursuit,
I finally began to read to see if,
after all my stalking other books
and stalling on this one,
I could find anything in the four Gospels
to illuminate the common lot of man in the world.
I read, and mused, and read,

112

and mused some more—
until I became completely oblivious
to the beauty around me.

Matthew 1:1. The book of the genealogy of Jesus Christ,
the son of David, the son of Abraham. . .

Luke 2:7. And she gave birth to her first-born son
and wrapped him in swaddling cloths,
and laid him in a manger,
because there was no place for them in the inn.

It is not true that you went into eclipse after creating
the universe and the world of man
and let your creation go its own capricious way.
You did once thrust yourself omnipotently
into the human scene and placed your eternal "I Am"
into the seed of a woman with a genealogy.
You made her cry with the pain of your birthing
and the joy "that a child is born into the world."
You curtailed and caged your omnipresence
to a speck of space in your universe,
abridged your Eternal Self to the time space
of one human life cut down in the prime of young manhood.
You let yourself be born nude and native
into the nullity and cruelty and rottenness
of life in this world.
You made yourself indigenous to the Absurd,
the life that extends
from contradiction to contradiction to death.

113

For it was not only the Gloria in Excelsis
that heralded your birth.
It was also the lamentation
of all the Jewish mothers of all
the boy babies two and under slain by King Herod
in Bethlehem and its environs:
A voice was heard in Ramah,
wailing and loud lamentation,
Rachel weeping for her children;
she refused to be consoled,
because they were no more.

Matthew 4:1. Then Jesus was led up by the Spirit
into the wilderness to be tempted by the devil.
And he fasted forty days and forty nights,
and afterward he was hungry.

Forty days and forty nights.
and not a word from Matthew about your physical suffering
during that fast, except to say matter-of-factly
"and afterward he was hungry."
If that were today the news reporters would have spun
each detail into columns of print,
for the more we the public regard personal suffering
as embarrassing, distressing, and unendurable,
the more avid and morbid we are to hear and read
accounts of the sufferings of others.
"Suffering" stories are to adults
like horror stories to children.

114

The Gospels make it plain that
you were not suffering for a public,
not even as an example to a public.
It was a purely voluntary personal suffering.
Why? Was it a tool, a means to an end?
A girding for action?
Was it a meaningful way to train your body
to bear the pains of the future?
Was it your way of mastering your body
so that you would no longer have to struggle
with its passions and pressures,
so that you could go without
food and water and sleep, if need be?
So that you could endure the passions and pressures
of a man's sexuality?
Was it simply and solely to empty
your body of all desires so that you could make
those three tremendous affirmations without
one reluctant, grudging, negative fraction of your self
whispering, "No!":

*Man shall not live by bread alone, but by
every word that proceeds from the mouth of God.
You shall not tempt the Lord your God.
You shall worship the Lord your God and him only
shall you serve.*

It is the affirmations the Gospel writers find important,
hence no morbid details to arouse
maudlin pity for the suffering Jesus
and no whys and wherefores for the suffering.
Not a hint of the beginning of a gospel of suffering here.

115

Matthew 9:35-37: And Jesus went about all the cities
and villages, teaching in their synagogues,
and preaching the gospel of the kingdom,
and healing every disease and every infirmity.
When he saw the crowds, he had compassion for them,
because they were harassed and helpless,
like sheep without a shepherd.

I felt the wingbeat of a thought, but read on.
Matthew 11:2-6: Now when John heard in prison about
the deeds of Christ, he sent word by his disciples
and said to him, "Are you he who is to come, or
shall we look for another?"
And Jesus answered them,
"Go and tell John what you hear and see:
the blind receive their sight and the lame walk,
lepers are cleansed and the deaf hear,
and the dead are raised up,
And the poor have good news preached to them.
And blessed is he who takes no offense at me."

Who are you, Jesus—
an Author, tasting the misery of the common man
for the sake of experiences that will go into a book
he plans to write about suffering?

Sage and Founder of a School of Suffering,
walking about in sandals, reciting its gospel
among the poor and lowly and suffering of the world?

116

bearded Social Activist agonizing
over the problem of suffering
and railing on the streetcorners against the injustices
and wickedness that cause suffering?

Preacher denouncing this accursed present generation
and ascribing all suffering to its sinfulness?

Government Fact Finder making a study
of human needs in a given area
with a view to drafting a new program to be called ACTION?

Knight of Resignation and Despair
going around and making the most
of a rotten situation?

You are none of these!
You are simply and solely God's I Am
incarnate in the flesh.
When you accepted human form,
you accepted evil and suffering
as a fact of life in this world.
The alchemy of No, of nonacceptance,
produces hatred, hostility, harshness, bitterness, malice.
The alchemy of your Yes to existential suffering
produced a compassion such as the world has never seen,
a life of living, loving, and giving
such as the world has never known.
You wasted no time agonizing over

117

the great wound of pain and suffering in creation
or in asking who dealt this wound.
You simply accepted it as the mystery of existence
and then devoted your life to healing it.
The crowd read in your eyes God's love for
them in their miserable condition
and flocked to you. The crowd laid bare
its painful, suffering wound,
and you touched the wound with your hand,
your most personal human hand—
and healed it.

No gospel of suffering in the Gospels, then—
just you—God's Yes to a suffering world.
No illumination of pain and suffering in the Gospels—
just you, God's I Am Love
radiantly and utterly illuminated.

My return from the gorge to the cabin
should have been made in a celebrant mood,
for I truly believed that,
like the Old Woman with her pig,
I had gotten over the stile and could get home—
if not that night, then the next.
Reflecting on the life of Jesus
had convinced me that the question
of pain and suffering
can be answered only in a life.
Suffering was, is, and will always remain
a mystery. It cannot be explained
or solved with words. In fact, giving
theoretical answers may lead to the conclusion

that the problem has been solved.
The mystery of pain and suffering
can only be answered with a life
which refuses to despair, handing one more
victory over to the forces of No,
but instead makes itself an instrument of Yes,
gives itself in love and compassion
to alleviate pain and suffering.
We may be driven to speculate upon, brood over,
agonize over the problem of suffering,
but ultimately and essentially we are to make ourselves
instruments of its alleviation.
This is what Jesus did.
This is what we are to do.
This is what I must do.
This is what Naomi,
awakened to misery and to mercy,
must do.

The only symbolic act I could think of
then and there to signalize this new meaning
was to dip my cup into the river
and water the ferns nature was trying to grow
in the tiny fissure gardens of huge boulders.
With no subsoil and no rain for two weeks,
the ferns were curling against their first unfurling,
and their newborn green was edged with brown.

But there was a maggot in my mood!
My mind seemed to be satisfied with this newest

and fullest meaning—but not my spirit.
The darkness of pain and suffering
had been greatly illuminated here on the river,
especially today in the gorge,
but there was still an unilluminated darkness
that could be felt by my spirit.
By the time I arrived at the cabin door
I knew what it was.

The illumination to which my mind
had said "Yes" in the gorge
had been light upon the *life* of Christ.
Yet all four Gospels march swiftly, deliberately,
and with dry eyes to the cross.
Apparently on eternity's scale
the death of Christ far outweighs the life of Christ!
In my pondering there in the gorge
I had simply taken the death on the cross to be
the overwhelming and culminating proof of Christ's
love and compassion for mankind.
Any other ending would have been
unequal to the life.
It would be like having Hamlet marry a Swedish princess
and become King of Denmark and father
of a robust royal family;
or Joan of Arc being rescued by an ardent admirer
just as the flames licked at her garments
and being carried away to a long and happy life
in a castle on the Rhone.

123

I shut the cabin door behind me,
leaned against it, and closed my eyes.
"All my life I have been taught and told, O Christ,
that you had to die on the cross to make reparation
to a God who demanded justice for a rebellious creation.
The very idea appalled me—and still does.
The cross has always been scandalous to my mind
and repulsive to my emotions—and still is.
Long ago I pushed that meaning away
as utterly offensive.
If the time has come for me to sit up and pay attention
to it, and if you are trying to tell me that your death
can illuminate the darkness of pain and suffering
even more than your life,
then knock at my brain house.
I suddenly find myself willing to listen,
although I doubt that I can ever believe it."

And then began what was not self-communing,
but more than a heightened consciousness
and less than a mystical experience.
I like to call it a cerebral happening,
and it happens when both my
consciousness and subconsciousness
have wrapped their sinewy arms and legs around
a question and hold it captive to my attention.
It happens when I have opened wide
all the doors and windows of my being
to any breeze, faint drumbeat,
or scent or gleam of perception.

It becomes a kind of running dialog
that is completely undiscriminating as to time and place.
It takes place at any hour,
in and out of bed, over an ironing board,
while weeding the garden, washing the dishes.
As I recall it, the dialog that late afternoon and evening
happened something like this:

*Place: The springbarrel, where I am dipping water
into a pail.*

NOT-I: Suppose that, in a new and thrilling dimension
of compassion and dedication to a cause,
men were able to heal all the sick and blind and dumb,
clothe all the poor, and feed all the hungry in the world.
Suppose that they were able to correct all
the economic and political conditions that cause
poverty, inequity, and wretchedness.
Would that put an end to pain and suffering?

I: I am sure that it would not.

NOT-I: Then there must be deeper roots for suffering
than natural infirmities
(including your granddaughter's brain damage).
There must be deeper roots than
economic insecurity and political injustice.
Where are these deeper roots that would not be touched
even by realizing the ideal of health, wealth,
liberty, and equality for all?

I: They are internal in man, not external.

Place: *Under the dark tent of the huge evergreen*
by the spring path
where I always set down the pail to rest.

Not-I: You just set down a heavy burden on a steep path.
If men were able to set down their heaviest
burden of suffering on the path of life,
it would be the consciousness of their sins.

I *(vehemently, and picking up my pail so abruptly*
that I slosh water on my feet.):
Not so! Now you're talking Sunday pulpit-prattle.
Modern man does NOT feel burdened by sin, and if you want
the plain truth, he yawns over the cross!

Place: *The cabin, where I am putting on dry socks.*

Not-I *(obviously trying another approach):* In this
tiny little community of cabins where you and your
close friends have brought your families
in July and August for some twenty years,
you are the one who knows the woods and river
better than any of them.
In your own mind you think of yourself as a combination
of a barefoot dryad of the forests and a river nymph.
(I nodding uncertainly, not knowing
whether I should feel guilty or proud.)
While the children sported in the river,

126

you went off by yourself. You all came back
to the cabin about the same time. Do you
remember how you felt as you came back?

I: Ecstatic! Beatific! At one with God, man,
and nature! Every string of my being in tune!

NOT-I: How long did this inner harmony last?

I: Until the first one in the family played out of tune
or someone in the community irritated or frustrated me.

NOT-I: Then your little community of family and friends
does not operate according to the laws of love,
which are the universal laws of being?

I: What family, what community does?

NOT-I: Why have you always been the pathmaker,
the woodgatherer, the watergetter
in this wilderness community? Why have you
all your life chosen tasks that give you solitude?

I *(beginning to understand)*: Because I long to feel
at one, in harmony, whole not fractured,
complete not incomplete, united not disunited.

NOT-I: When you are in solitude,
you sometimes fantasize, day-dream situations and
relationships.

127

At such times does your imagination create harmony
or disharmony, unity or disunity?

I: Always coherence, always completeness,
always wholeness, always oneness!

Not-I: Do you have *one* actual, rather than fantasized,
human relationship that you can say is complete,
harmonious, unbroken, and continuous?
Where you feel completely at one with the other?
A relationship of transparent love and joy?

I: No, not one!

Not-I: Why are you crying?

I *(savagely):* Because I have so recently been
deprived of my last illusion of such a friendship!
The wound is still raw.

Not-I: Would you call it anguish?

I: Yes, it qualifies as anguish—
the anguish of alienation,
loneliness, of not being in relationship.
A void where I was so sure
there was a touching of spirits.

Not-I: Whose was the fault? Whose the flaw?

I: Mine as well as the other's.

128

This ended the dialog that night,
for when both the consciousness and subconsciousness
wrap themselves around self-pity
and the I is wholly engrossed in feeling sorry for itself,
dialog with any other is impossible.

But the dialog began again the moment
I opened my eyes the next morning.
In fact, it was as if the Not-I had waited
patiently at the door of consciousness
the entire night and came in with the sound
of the river and the chill of the morning.
I curled up in the warm nest of blankets
and decided to carry on this dialog in bed for a while.

I: You became a bit too personal last night.

Not-I: The roots of pain and suffering
are deep in the person.
This is where pain and suffering
have to be addressed.

131

I: Well, you touched rock-bottom last night:
man's alienation from man,
the impossibility of an unbroken, continuous
relationship of transparent love and joy,
the anguish of this alienation.
For men's deepest longing and need
is for such a relationship.

Not-I: Are you sure that man's alienation
from man is the rock-bottom anguish
of man's spirit? Suppose that men,
spurred on by sensational new knowledge
about the human mind, were able to alter
undesirable behavior patterns and produce
a better humanity.
What if they could really liberate men from
the contradictions of their subliminal selves
and make them ethical heroes of a sort—
filled with noble, selfless sentiments,
impatient with mediocrity and self-seeking,
disdaining money, renouncing personal ambition,
working with singleness of mind and religious
zeal to transform profoundly the world
and achieve a temporal salvation for mankind.
Suppose men by incredible vitality and
selfless involvement were to achieve this ideal;
suppose they could in fact live lives of compassion
as close to the life Jesus lived on this earth
as is humanly possible.
Would that put an end to pain and suffering?

132

I *(so vehemently that I leaped out of bed
and was quite oblivious to the cabin cold):*
No! For they would know the pain and suffering
of inevitable failure.
Why do you plague me with such thoughts?
After all, I am living in the last half
of the 20th century, the most convincing evidence
against any theory of progress.
I know what you are trying to do:
corner me into a consciousness of sin!
But you won't ever catch me in the sin of optimism—
be it Marxist Utopianism
or the American Great Society!

*Place: Two hours later, sawing and chopping wood
outside the sauna.*

I: What you were trying to lead me to see, of course,
was that there is a deeper root to pain and suffering
than disharmony between men
and that even if men achieved the impossible
and cured that disharmony,
men would still know pain and suffering.
The church says this is because men face eternal damnation.
But something in me protests this stress
on saving my own soul,
on getting myself saved for eternity.
This emphasis on the beyond does not appeal to me.
I have no particular yen
to be everlasting. As for the "making my peace

with my Maker" approach, I feel, like Thoreau,
that we have never really quarreled.

Not-I: You seem to have experienced the joy and bliss
of close human relationships,
of being related to a person in a love
that is transparent and without judgment,
accepting the other's whole being in joy,
and feeling yourself accepted by the other in the same way.

I: Yes, there have been some such relationships
in my life, but they never remained
so simple, lucid, honest, and open.

Not-I: You do, however, deeply desire them
to remain so. You do long to have
these relationships be continuous, unbroken, unchanged?

I: Yes, these relationships that stir
the roots of my whole being to April joy—
I do truly desire them to remain
forever April.
But they never do!
They remain relationships,
but they become cloudy and November.

Not-I: Do you believe in God as Eternal Spirit and Being
who created you to be spirit and being
with whom he may live in a relationship
that stirs the roots of your whole self,
awakens you to the possibility of becoming

134

what he created you to be?
A relationship where you know that he loves you utterly—
and utterly as you are—
in fact, loves you for the you-ness of you,
the special, particular, individual, personal,
unique, original you-ness of you?

I *(startled)*: You make him sound like a lover!

Not-I: Which he is.

I: What about the judge part?

Not-I: Men never come before a judge as committees,
clubs, crowds, or congregations—
always as single individuals.
In this sense God is called a judge,
for we live our lives before him as individuals,
accountable to him as single, solitary
individuals:

I *(firmly)*: Yes, I do believe in God who is spirit
who created me spirit to live in relationship with him.

Not-I: Is your relationship to God one of transparent
love and joy, unbroken and continuous?

I: Sometimes I feel that it is
and sometimes I feel that it isn't.
(I stop short, silenced by the illogic of my answer.)

All right, it is *not* unbroken and continuous.
It is very episodic.

Not-I: Do you anguish that it is episodic?

I *(throwing the ax in a fury):* Will you shut up and leave me
alone!
And what in heaven or hell
does this have to do with Nani!

A half hour later in the sauna,
where I had built a small fire
and lay on the top shelf looking out the window
at the river, the dialog resumed.

I *(humbly)*: Why is it so episodic?
Why do I feel "in relationship"
for three weeks, maybe,
and "out of relationship" for six months?
Now don't tell me it's because I have never
been converted, never accepted Christ,
never thrown myself at
the Throne of Grace, etc. etc.

NOT-I: You have never accepted the death
of Christ on the cross for your sins.

I *(angrily)*: Here we are, right back
where we started! I repeat that I do not feel
particularly sinful! I happen to be
living in an age of relativities,
and by the relativities in which we now live
I am relatively adequate.

NOT-I: You agree that God is a God of love
and that the laws of being
are the laws of love.

I: Yes, wholeheartedly.
I can even recite it. Luke 10:27: "You shall love
the Lord your God
with all your heart, and with all your soul,
and with all your strength,
and with all your mind;
and your neighbor as yourself."

NOT-I: Would you agree that God's law of love
is absolute? You do not accuse yourself
of murder, theft, or unchastity, but
do you ever accuse yourself
of not having loved enough? Or do you
feel that you love quite adequately?

I: I never said that!

NOT-I: But you did!
(after a long silence) I know what you are doing:
making a catalog of particular times

140

when you did not live by the absolute law of love.
You are making a list of specific people
whom you do not love by the absolute law of love.
But God is not interested in your particulars,
only in your condition;
for the particulars are the result of the condition.
It is your condition that is sin,
and the particulars are the consequences of the condition.
The condition is infinitely worse than the particulars.
The lynching of a black man is not as sinful
as the condition that caused it.
Long before the lynching
the condition clamored for the act.
Stop thinking of the hostile and disturbed girl
you did not take into your home
when it appeared that she would be disruptive
and would require much more attentive love and time
than you felt you had to give.
Think instead of the condition that prompted
that guilty No. Think of the dark No
that lives within you, that battles to be the master
passion of your spirit.

I: O.K., you win. My condition is such
that I can never love either God or man
as God requires me to love.
Therefore I am alienated from both God and man.
Therefore I anguish. This is the secret root
of man's despair, of his pain and suffering!
Now are you satisfied?

Well, I am not!
My mind still boggles at the cross.

NOT-I: Think of a relationship to the person of God
in the most superlative human terms you know,
it would still be woefully inadequate.
Think of it as a relationship where you are ever becoming.
It is not a relationship devoid of pain and suffering,
but even the pain and suffering are turned
into instruments of your becoming.
Knowing such a relationship, would you wish it
to be terminated at your death?
Could you face an eternity of no relationship,
of Nothingness?
Does not your whole being
deeply long that such a relationship—
which here on earth you know only in part—
be a perpetual union,
unbroken, continuous, and unchanged?

I: O yes! A dying into nothingness,
losing such a relationship,
would be—Hell!

NOT-I: This is why Christ died on the cross
and was raised again, absurd as it seems.
Had he merely lived a life of pure compassion here on earth,
you would not have the possibility
of this eternal relationship to the Eternal.
Had he merely died,
he would not have given you the possibility

142

of this eternal relationship to God.
God as man had to assume human existence broadly,
all its absurdity, all its pain,
all its suffering, all its terror.
God as man had to experience being bent and broken,
had to know the absolute despair
of alienation and forsakenness.
He had to cry from the shuddering depths of his being
man's cry of despair, alienation, and aloneness:
"My God, my God, why hast Thou forsaken me?"
He had to belong so entirely to the human
rottenness present in the Absurd
that he had to die as a sinner on a criminal's gibbet
for man's condition of sin.
He had to taste in time the bitterness
of eternal isolation from God
so that you may have eternal relationship with him.
To bridge the abyss between time and eternity
he had to descend into the abyss.

I: It still sounds like a scheme hatched below
and not in the heavenly courts of love!

Not-I: If it had been a scheme hatched below,
it would not have involved suffering and death
on a cross. The hero that the mastermind
of the subcontinent of No would advance
would not be a suffering servant.
He would be a colossal hero—
if not in fact, then in fiction;
for the Madison Avenue of the capital city of No

143

would cunningly construct a colossal image
for their savior of the human race.
Shrewd as he is, the mastermind of No
cannot conceive of a redeemer who is as penniless
and powerless as a beggar,
who suffers and dies the shockingly ignominious death
meted out to the most despicable enemies of society.

I *(whispering):* The inverse laws of spirit.

NOT-I: Right! In a way the cross is a de-creation,
a shattering of human values.
For it was not a great ethical hero
triumphantly testing his soul and endurance
who died on the cross,
but the Son of God testifying in his human nature
to human misery—
and in his divine nature testifying that God
the Father of all mankind
loves his creation immersed in its misery.

I: Stop right there!
I still cannot see how the cross
affects man's misery here and now.
And don't forget my Nani and my Naomi!

NOT-I: The cross affects men's misery here and now
by curing the self-loathing and despair
that eat at the marrowbone of the human spirit.
The human spirit knows what the human mind may not know.
(Incidentally, what the mind knows does not seem

144

to exercise much influence on the lives of men.)
The human spirit knows self-loathing,
because the human spirit knows that it completely
fails to live by the eternal laws of love.
The human spirit knows *despair,*
because the human spirit knows that it is impossible
to live by the eternal laws of love
and therefore cannot hope or expect to live
in relationship to the God of love
and therefore has lost relationship to the God of love
now and for all eternity.
The human spirit knows this
even if the mind does not.
But the God of love says,
"Yes, I offer you the possibility
of unbroken relationship.
Here on the cross in the broken body of my son
is my offer of unbroken relationship to me.
Here is my 'Yes, you are forgiven.'
Here is my guarantee of a totally new relationship,
a new creation—Faith,
faith in my beloved son.
The opposite of sin and despair is no longer virtue;
it is faith in my son."
If God's Yes incarnate in the flesh had not suffered,
you who suffer would feel superior to him.
You would in your superiority say No to him.
Do not pass lightly over that cry,
"My God, my God, why hast Thou forsaken me?"
It is that cry of desolation,

that cry out of the temporary eclipse of God,
the silence of God, the darkness of no dialog—
it is that cry which draws you out of your own darkness.
That cry silences the spirit of No in you,
the spirit of defiance and despair.
It summons forth your Yes.

I: Yes to what?

NOT-I: Not to a body of affirmations, not to a new
patchwork, not to a new program of action,
not to a new struggle to be virtuous and worthy,
but Yes to him who suffered and died on the cross
for your sinful condition.

And I? I had not a word more to say.
There on the top shelf of the sauna
I skimmed the Gospels once more in the light
of this most recent illumination,
and it was there all right, just as Not-I had said!

I have come that men may have life
and have it in its fullness.
I am the way.
I am the truth.
I am the door.
I am the true vine.
I am the resurrection and the life.
Unless a grain of wheat falls into the earth
and dies, it remains alone:
but if it dies it bears much fruit.

146

Late that night, I, who all my life had said Yes
to the life of Christ but had never really
said Yes to his death on the cross,
said a most ungrudging Yes to that, too.
Having done so, I did not experience any mystical
exaltation, not even a vivid relief.
I did not shout "Hallelujah" to the rafters,
but deep down where the meanings are,
and deeper still, where the spirit is,
there was a brightening and an eastering
that had not been there before.

I awoke the next morning to what I knew
would be my last day on the river
until my Partner and I returned in July
and the children and grandchildren filtered back
for their too short vacations.
The cup of Lake Superior we can see
from our high point on the river
was Copenhagen blue.
Knowing that the sun would stay the day,
I descended to the river with a pillow and a book
and settled down on the Giantess' Lap.

Whenever I experience any kind of a significant
illumination of a blurred, confused meaning,

149

I skim Scripture from Genesis to Revelation
and let this new light fall on the "old stuff."
It never fails, and it did not fail today;
the "old stuff" became as modern
as my most recent heartbeat.
The whole Old Testament was the story
of my own spiritual life: responding
to external events rather than being directed
by and from an internal event;
responding in ecstasy to glorious happenings,
feeling dull, dead, and despondent
when there were none.
Sometimes yeasty and buoyant,
Sometimes sour and dull.
Always episodic.

When Moses came down from Mount Sinai
the skin of his face shone because
he had been talking with God.

But skin-glow of Word-flame faded;
the bright alive of oneness gloomed.
Thereafter was ever thus:
a descent into the existential,
an eclipse of rapture.
Afterward was always a slow dissolving,
a glow-setting.
The afterglow was nice
while it lasted, Lord God;

but it always died
in your silence

until

until you put your whole self into your Word,
until your Word became flesh and blood and
lived among us,
until that flesh was torn and that blood was shed
for us,
until talking with you was no longer a matter
of climbing a mountain to you
but of you descending to us
until you conversed with man in your Son
and on the cross.

In Christ the Son
Nows of glow
Glows of Now
Eternal Now
Eternal Glow.

Halfway through the Gospels, I stopped my swift skimming,
laughed aloud, and struck the ancient boulder
with the palms of my hands.
"Oh, you Rock of my Salvation,
all those stale old cliches are true.
O ye angels, archangels, seraphims, and cherubims,
don't swoon or faint there in your invisible kingdom,

but I feel like shouting a song to the river,
a song that has veritably embarrassed
me all my life!"

Spirit-tippled and Word-bibbed,
I did sing there on the river with gusto:

Just as I am, without one plea,
But that Thy blood was shed for me,
And that Thou bid'st me come to Thee,
O Lamb of God, I come, I come!

After that bit of wholly satisfying intemperance,
I moved to the Table Rock and lay for a long time
looking down into the river.

The thought came to me that somewhere recently
I had read about the discovery of an ancient scroll
containing sayings ascribed to Jesus
not recorded in the four Gospels.
One of them, as I recalled it, was,
"Turn over any stone,
and I am there."
Figuratively, at least, the words were true.
I had turned over the heavy stone
of the pain and suffering of Nani
and had found Christ there.
I had a feeling that any pain problem,
the front side of any question at which one stares fixedly—
has the same backside.

Turn it over, and there one finds Christ.
The frontsides of questions may be different.
The backsides are always the same.
"Turn over any stone,
and there I am."

But Nani was, is, and will remain
a burden and a source of pain.
Moreover, she could never even begin to comprehend
any of the meanings that had come to me here on the river.
What grace was there for her—*directly*—
in all this grace?
Oh, I knew there were hosts of "indirectlies,"
and they would be flocking into my mind very soon.
But directly?

If Naomi had lived contemporary
with Jesus Christ of Nazareth,
she would have brought her baby to him,
and he would have taken Nani in his arms,
put his hand upon her head,
and healed her directly.
But what direct thing could he do for Nani now?
Or for all the others who could never rise
on the intellectual scale above idiocy?
Or those who in the senility of old age
had gradually slid down the scale of intelligence
to imbecility and vacuity?
I thought of the father of a dear friend,
a vigorous, intelligent, gifted leader of the church

who in his last years became so *absent*-minded
that he simply lay and babbled numbers.
Is being absent-in-mind
synonymous with being absent-in-spirit?
To have faith do we need to have enough mind to grasp
the meaning of faith?
To be in the relationship of faith to God the Father,
do we need a measurable IQ?

A vehement "No!" brought me to my feet.
I threw a stone so hard against Gog
that it bounced to Magog
and on each boulder raised a smoke
that floated back to my nostrils with the acrid smell
of an exploded firecracker.

The meaning of life is in the relationship
of the whole person to God,
not in the relationship of the cerebellum.
The relationship to God is possible in Christ
for every individual
from Einstein—to Nani.
Men in pity and sympathy go down
to a certain level of intelligence
to admit fellow-beings to their man-made heavens,
but then disgust, horror, and scorn take over and say,
"No, such a non-human as you cannot come in."
But God's love descends lower and takes the lowest.
Indeed, his eyes see no difference at all
between an Einstein and a cretin.
I thought of my friend's father.

154

When the tenuous tape
coiled on the reel of his memory
no longer tensible
broke
and in his patching and repairing
he fused incompatible pieces,

When the tenacious thread of memory
frayed and flaccid
slackened, bunched, knotted
and finally unravelled
into a tortuous, twisted tangle,

When others heard the twang of breaking memory
and saw the shattered fragments of what was mind
and murmured sorrowfully,
"How tragic!
He was a giant in his day!"

The Lord God picked up the fumbled, jumbled words
the topsy-turvey alphabet
the whole embarrassing litter
and it was as if they rearranged themselves
into a liturgy of praise!

And it was so.
The Lord God looked
and, behold, it was very good.

When the contours of ideas blurred and eclipsed
the colors of emotions faded out
and words themselves grew vague and meaningless,
when even word-sounds
vowels and consonants
retained no meaning,

When—strangely—
as he lay in his long dying—
numbers became his living language
and he intoned them one by one
tirelessly
hour upon hour
day after day
as time tallied its final count for him,

When others stood beside his bed
and heard his babbling numbers
and tiptoed tearfully away,

the Lord God gathered up the digits and the ciphers
the sum total of his numbers
the whole untidy chaos
and they added up!
and their sum was—adoration!

And it was so.
The Lord God looked
and, behold, it was very good.

156

When, finally,
he lay in a dimension that was no dimension
in the deep beyond and far behind of subconsciousness,

When eyes betrayed no flutter of thought
and all that stirred in him
was feeble, faltering breath
and tired faithful heart,

When others could not bear to see
and called what they saw
"just existing,"

The Lord God looked into the abandoned house
where not even dried autumn leaves drifted,
shifted absurdly
across the bleached warped floor.
The Lord God saw
not the empty vastness
but the vast givenness
that was and is and evermore shall be!

And it was so.
The Lord God looked
and, behold, it was very good.

As I had expected, hosts of "indirectlies"
began crowding into my mind on the heels
of this direct meaning for Nani.
But I dismissed them politely
and asked them to wait for the long drive home the next day.

I had a task to do, a promise to Naomi to keep.
It was to put her beloved river in a box
and send it to her.

Into the plastic-lined box
which I airmailed the next day went

ten rust-red, blue-gray smooth pebbles
nine tablespoons of the rich mold of a perished pine
eight tiny fairy cups in a bed of moss
seven bark "grotesques" designed by the river
and weathered by the sun
six bright green cones of an evergreen
five "stars of the north," the flowers of the bunchberry
four tablespoons of amber water from the river
three curls of birch bark
two tiny ferns
one microscopic cedar tree.

After locking the cabin door,
I went to the river to say goodbye
and, of course, I was beguiled to linger—
to sun, to swim,
and even to lie on my favorite rock
and read my favorite author.
In the seventh chapter I found the fitting words
of farewell.
I had come to the river in the mood of Psalm 42:

I say to God, my rock:
"Why hast thou forgotten me?
Why go I mourning
because of the oppression of the enemy?"

161

As with a deadly wound in my body,
my adversaries taunt me
while they say to me continually,
"Where is your God?"

Why are you cast down, O my soul,
and why are you disquieted within me?
Hope in God; for I shall again praise him,
my help and my God.

I left the river with John's words singing
in my ears like the symphony of the river:

On the last day of the feast, the great day,
Jesus stood up and proclaimed,
"If any one thirst, let him come to me
and drink. He who believes in me, as
the scripture has said, 'Out of his heart
shall flow rivers of living water.'"
Now this he said about the Spirit,
which those who believed in him
were to receive.

So that was how the third member of the Trinity
fit in!
God, the rock of steadfast love
before whom our human love is but a grain of sand.
Christ, the living water, in whom we have forgiveness of sins,
in whom, buoyant and free, we can float
in the existential life of contradictions and suffering.

162

And Spirit, poured into our human spirits
to help us say our weak and faltering Yes,
flowing out of our spirits a river of living water
to bathe and lave the pain and suffering of the world.

"Oh, you Reality, so aptly pictured by rocks,
living water, and flowing streams!
No wonder I love this white water river!" I thought,
and slid once more into the parable of the river
to float buoyantly and swim boldly in its waters,
at ease and quite at home.

After mailing the box of river
at the first post office on the shore
(so that the gift would have an "up north" postmark),
I drove the 300 miles home without stopping.
As I had fully expected, the thoughts still trooped in,
which meant that the attention of my whole being
was still centered on the question of pain and suffering.
Some were No thoughts, but this, too, I expected
and will continue to expect until I die into
the utterly illumined kingdom of Yes.
But since there was no longer any possibility
of the No forces taking over my spirit,
I did not tremble and despair before them any more.
I simply let my Yes answer them.

No: Why the elation? Was it such a big deal up there
on the river? After all, pain is still pain

and suffering is still suffering,
and Nani is still Nani.

YES: True, pain is still pain
and suffering is still suffering
and Nani is still Nani,
but the deepest root of human suffering
is cut by the cross,
and the human spirit is released from its worst
anxiety and dread: anxiety about death,
the dread of dying into nothingness,
total extinction, dying into total and permanent
isolation from the eternal God.
To be released from suffering that dread about eternity
sets one free for the struggle in time.

NO: What struggle?

YES: Against *you!* Against your forces of No
within and without
that create most of the pain and suffering in this life.

*(A detour for road construction and a trailing traffic cop
silenced the dialog for a time, but it resumed again.)*

NO: We are uncomfortably aware, some of us,
that a revolution is taking place,
but it seems to us that you Christians in the past
have been so interested in the "beyond"
and in saving your own souls

164

that you have been callous to injustice
and indifferent to suffering other than your own.
We have a cynical saying that
no man dies of another's wound,
and we don't see many of you dying
or even suffering for another's wound.
We, of course, rejoice in the fact.

YES: I would be the last to deny that.
It is the sin of Christendom
that we live and die as if Christ suffered and died
to provide us with a cozy untroubled life
and a peaceful death.
But the Spirit is always convicting us of that sin.
(Please note that the church is constantly
being healed from within!)
The Spirit is always producing suffering servants
who refuse to despair over the world,
who do not isolate themselves
from the pain and suffering of men, but say:
"Life is absurd; we are part of it.
The world is full of pain and suffering;
it is ours."
And to the degree that they accept
life's absurdity and pain,
to that same degree they offer their lives
to alleviate human misery.

Then I myself, speaking for myself,
said aloud, in a "try and top this" spirit,

"And they love God in and through and beyond
their own sufferings.
They curse neither the pain nor God for allowing it.
They simply offer their lives to it,
and they praise.
Francis of Assisi did not curse leprosy;
he kissed the leper and praised God.
Martin Luther King did not curse the cancer of racism;
he walked in the streets with his suffering brother—
and praised God!"

The voice of No was silenced for a time,
but it came back for one last attempt to stir up
distress in my spirit,
addressing me directly, not my Yes.

No: What about Nani? What about Naomi?
I suppose now that you have thought so hard
about this matter, you will feel
obliged to lecture, sermonize, moralize.

I: A frightful temptation! But Naomi will have to do
as every human has to do:
confront the stark truths of self,
confront pain and suffering,
confront the cross—
all by herself.
She will have to discover for herself
whether she loves God on the level of a family
of lovely, lively, bright children,

or deeper down, farther back, and behind that.
I shall continue to pray
that she not be plunged into a nightmare,
that she accept the suffering and through it is awakened
to mercy, love, and joy.

No: I'm curious. What is the first thing
you will do about the problem when you get home?

I: In the first place
I shall no longer call Nani a problem—
or, for that matter, any source of pain and suffering
that has no solution.
Such pain and suffering is a mystery.
A problem is like that road block back there,
something that looms up before the self,
obstructing its passage, frustrating
and interfering with its normal progress,
spoiling the self's pleasant life.
One fine day the problem, like that road block,
may not be there;
the whole clumsy obstruction may be gone.
But a mystery—a mystery is not simply a barrier
which looms up before the self,
some big negative something to be pushed away
or put back where it was.
Nor is it a heavy something on top of the self,
a huge boulder crushing the self. A mystery is something
which the self finds itself caught up into.
The self can never really see the mystery in its entirety,

know it in its fullness,
because the self is not outside of it
but is within it, is a part of it.
Or the mystery may be said to be within the self.
Since the mystery is within the self
it does not paralyze the self or make it motionless.
It sets the self in motion.
Please understand that this is not
a self-starting, self-propelling motion.
It is the power of the divine Yes
leading the self to say Yes to the suffering.
Even though the self may continue to be a suffering self,
in and through the power of the divine Yes
it becomes a serving self, a loving self.
It addresses the mystery of pain and suffering
with its life.

No: Ha! I thought you were not going to
lecture, sermonize, or moralize.

I: I said I would not lecture, sermonize, or moralize
to Naomi, but, believe me,
whenever you or any other voice of No
begins to badger me,
I shall clobber you with Truth.
You asked me what is the first thing
I will do about "the problem" when I get home.
I will bake a loaf of my incomparable bread
and send it to Naomi.
Then I shall buy the prettiest dress in town for Nani.

As soon as I can manage it I shall go to Hawaii,
where I will hold Nani,
rock her, sing to her.

No: She cannot hear!

I *(firmly)*: I will sing to her.
Do you know what I shall sing?

Praise him,
Praise him,
All ye little children;
God is love,
God is love.

This really silenced No.
Apparently the voices of No
are completely routed by praise.
It was a joyful discovery!

The closer I came to home, the more aware I became
that my being, conscious and unconscious,
was loosening its hold on the question
of pain and suffering.
It was as if its legs and arms relaxed and disengaged
themselves mile after mile,
until by the time I opened the door of home
and was engaged by other arms,
the grilling and probing and sifting and separating
were stilled.

169

Much later that evening I read the accumulated mail,
the letters from Naomi first.
One paragraph leaped out at me:
"I have been happy these last months—full of joy.
I mean full of joy.
I wish I could paint "full of joy."
It's beautiful!
Yet it has been during my joy that my deepest,
most honest grief has come.
I feel both inside.
There's no conflict.
I think they build onto each other.
It's strange!"

Strange, yes!
A mystery which the creature of the first spontaneity,
"the natural man," cannot understand
without a profound change taking place deep within
where the meanings are,
and deeper still, where the spirit is.
And it was happening!
Yes, it *is* happening.
And will go on happening.

"It looks as if our Naomi has found what you found on our
river—the Catskill eagle," said my Partner.

"The Catskill eagle?"

Then my Partner took from the shelf his well-thumbed
copy of Melville's *Moby Dick* and read:

There is a wisdom that is woe;
but there is a woe that is madness.
And there is a Catskill eagle in some souls
that can alike dive down into the blackest gorges,
and soar out of them again and become invisible
in the sunny spaces. And even if he forever
flies within the gorge, that gorge is in the mountains,
so that even in his lowest swoop the mountain eagle
is still higher than other birds upon the plain,
even though they soar.

"It fits! It fits!" I cried in excitement.
It's in Isaiah!

But they who wait for the Lord
shall renew their strength,
they shall mount up with wings
like eagles.

With her husband, Dr. Howard Hong of St. Olaf College, Edna Hong is well-known as a translator of the writings of Søren Kierkegaard. In 1968 the Hongs won the National Book Award for their translation of the first volume of Kierkegaard's *Journals and Papers.* Among Mrs. Hong's other books is the popular *Clues to the Kingdom.* She is the mother of eight children and grandmother of nine and now lives in Northfield, Minnesota.